F I R S T STORY

First Story aims to celebrate and foster creativity, literacy and talent in young people. We're cheerleaders for books, stories, reading and writing. We've seen how creative writing can build students' self-esteem and self-confidence.

We place acclaimed authors as writers-in-residence in state schools across the country. Each author leads weekly after-school workshops for up to sixteen students. We publish the students' work in anthologies and arrange public readings and book launches at which the students can read aloud to friends, families and teachers.

For more information and details of how to support First Story, see www.firststory.org.uk or contact us at info@firststory.co.uk.

Eureka!
ISBN 978-0-85748-058-3

Published by First Story Limited
www.firststory.org.uk
4 More London Riverside
London
SE1 2AU

Typesetter: Avon DataSet Ltd
Cover designer: Todd Oliver
Printed in the UK by Intype Libra Ltd

First Story is a registered charity number 1122939 and a private company limited by guarantee incorporated in England with number 06487410. First Story is a business name of First Story Limited.

Eureka!

An Anthology
BY THE FIRST STORY GROUP
AT NOTTINGHAM ACADEMY, GREENWOOD ROAD

EDITED AND INTRODUCED BY CLARE BROWN | 2012

Fostering creativity, literacy and talent

Contents

INTRODUCTION	*Clare Brown and Jason Philip*	9
From the Sixth Form Group		
I Remember 1	*Fatima S Khan*	11
I Remember 2		12
So Close...		14
This One's for the Invigilators		15
FORK!	*Fridah Risper Nzaba*	16
Board 1 : 0 Me		18
Young Black Enterprise		19
I Remember	*Isabel Perez*	21
Untitled!		23
The Playground of Jealousy		24
How Many Times Have You Played the Guitar?		25
Biographies	*Sixth Form Group*	26

From the Year Seven Group

My Name Is...	*Monet Dinall-Coley*	28
The Weather		29
How to Live a Happy Life		30
The Hurricane	*Zachary C Douglas*	31
Tsunami		32
Nick Parker Does Something Unexpected	*Jake Lawrence Dunn*	33
Seasons		34
How to Jump to the Moon		35
I Am...		36
To Live a Happy Life you Need to...	*Robyn Gill*	37
I Am Me		38
How to Train a Unicorn	*Lucy Megan Guiblin*	39
How To Prepare for a Trip to Mars	*Kia Johnson Norton*	40
I Am Not Amazing at Lying		41
When Julie Meets Rainbow	*Nyall Wright*	42
How to Get Your Pet Talking Monkey, Steve to Do What you Want		43
Biographies	*Year Seven Group*	44

Thank You

Melanie Curtis at Avon DataSet for her overwhelming support for First Story and for giving her time in typesetting this anthology.

Kate Kunac-Tabinor and all the designers at **OUP** for their overwhelming support for First Story and **Todd Oliver** specifically for giving his time in designing the cover for this anthology.

Intype Libra for printing this anthology at a discounted rate and **Moya Birchall** and **Tony Chapman** of Intype for their advice.

HRH the Duchess of Cornwall, Patron of First Story

The Trustees of First Story:
Beth Colocci, Charlotte Hogg, Rob Ind, Andrea Minton Beddoes, John Rendel, Alastair Ruxton, David Stephens, Sue Horner and James Wood.

The Advisory Board of First Story:
Andrew Adonis, Julian Barnes, Jamie Byng, Alex Clark, Julia Cleverdon, Andrew Cowan, Jonathan Dimbleby, Mark Haddon, Simon Jenkins, Andrew Kidd, Rona Kiley, Chris Patten, Kevin Prunty, Deborah Rogers, Zadie Smith, William Waldegrave, and Brett Wigdortz.

Thanks to:
Jane and Peter Aitken, Ed Baden-Powell, Laura Barber, The Blue Door Foundation, Josie Cameron-Ashcroft, Anthony Clake, Molly Dallas, The Danego Charitable Trust, Peter and Genevieve Davies, Martin Fiennes, the First Story Events Committee, the First Story First Edition Club, Alex Fry, The Funding Network, Goldman Sachs Gives, Kate Harris, Kate Kunac-Tabinor, the John R. Murray Charitable Trust, Old Possum's Trust, Oxford

University Press, Philip Pullman, Pitt Rivers Museum, Quercus Books, Radley College, the Sigrid Rausing Trust, Clare Reihill, The Royal Society of Literature, Chris Smith, The Staples Trust, Teach First, Betsy Tobin, Richard Tresidder, Walker Books and Hannah Westland.

Most importantly we would like to thank the students, teachers and writers who have worked so hard to make First Story a success this year.

Introduction

Clare Brown and Jason Philip

Nottingham Academy's second year of participation in First Story has operated at both ends of the school's age range: Year Seven and Sixth Form. The two groups have come together on a few (always lively and sometimes surprising) occasions but have, in the main, operated separately, with Jason Philip heading up the younger students and Clare Brown working mostly with a small group of Sixth Formers.

Despite the difference in their ages, the students have followed the same broad 'curriculum' of exercises and discussions, and it has been a delight to see how gamely the younger writers have risen to the challenges this has presented. The atmosphere in their weekly after-school sessions has always crackled with ideas and enthusiasm and they have become progressively bolder and more confident about using, and expressing, the power of their imagination.

Our thoughtful 6th Form group, despite having to juggle First Story with the responsibilities of A Level study along with work and family commitments, have been focussed on making the most of their creativity. Whether writing stories, poems, scripts or some of the happily indefinable pieces of work the sessions produced, they have been open to experimentation and supportive of one another's adventures in writing.

Between them, the groups have produced a rich variety of writing, and we hope you enjoy spending some time in the worlds they have imagined, peopled with unicorns, super-heroes and extreme weather events, and reading about the more familiar worlds of their own experience which they have described with great poignancy and wit.

The title of the book comes from the moments we all experienced during our sessions; when an idea emerged unexpectedly, like the sun on a cloudy day, and the words began to flow.

We would like to thank Aaron Belcher, a First Story veteran from last year, for giving up his time to take part in many of our workshops; his input has been very much appreciated. Our thanks also go to all of the students who have taken part and contributed to this anthology.

Clare Brown and Jason Philip

I Remember: 1

Fatima S Khan

I remember it was mid-December. Me and two of my cousins (with opposite personalities) were counting the stars that made the night sky look so magical.

'Thirty-two!' said one of them.

'No, it's thirty-five!' said the other one.

I got thirty-three but did not say it, as my mind had wandered off the counting game. Instead I was thinking: where were the clouds? It's winter, and that's when the clouds come, right? But soon I forgot the question and became somewhat thankful.

It seemed as if these stars had come to bid me goodbye, like most of my relatives. It was my last night in this house, the house that had been home for me all my life.

Another one of my cousins shouted from the inside: 'Come inside already! The sky in England will be the same.'

The other two next to me laughed. All I could say was, 'You never know,' and after thirty-odd hours it turned out that... we really didn't know. We had no idea at all.

I Remember: 2

Fatima S Khan

I remember
It was mid-December.
The fragrance of hot pakoras
And the sweet 'n sour sauces' aromas
Flew across the mansion,
Even the walls detected the action.
As the clock stuck seven,
Just a few hours left now, about eleven.

I remember
The rectangular eraser,
I won it during the previous year.
That memory – it's not so clear.
I wanted to take it with me
And hold onto the win with glee
But the thought slipped away soon.
Bang! It burst somewhere, like a balloon.

I remember
The light going amber,
Bidding farewell to the old fort,
Arriving at the cryptic airport.

The ride flying up into the clouds,
Watching all the trolleys pass by,
And waking up to a brand new sky.

So Close...

Fatima S Khan

She almost jumped
Into those deep waters.
Her toes were even kissed
By the crazy currents.
The thoughts in her tiny head
Built high barriers.
You may call her a coward
But she could hear the screams
That were waiting ahead
For me… her… you… us.

This One's for the Invigilators

Fatima S Khan

You come here to invigilate
As we show up for our exams.
We try our best to co-operate,
But your 'click-a-ty clack-a-ty' shoes
Make us wanna annihilate
Both the tables and the chairs.
Plz, no time to debate.
Just keep them away from our base.
Kindly, don't push us to counteract
And let us work the case!
Respectfully,
The students.

FORK!

Fridah Risper Nzaba

DID THAT GET YOUR ATTENTION?

Bill: I told you to put my fork on the right-hand side. Why is my egg on top of the beans, eh?

Jane: Sorry Bill, I forgot. I had a long day in the office.

Bill: Well, I'm not eating this.

Jane: Honey, please eat some; you need to get some food down you.

Bill: Well move my fork then.

Jane: Why are you so bothered?

Bill: Fine, I'm not eating this. Feed this horrible food to the fat cat.

Jane: Oh, I spent ages making that for you honey. You should just appreciate me more.

Bill: Why should I if you can't even cook and you can't even place the forks right?

Jane: Right, I will make some more for you. How was your day?

Bill: It was good before I came home to find my fork on the damn left.

Jane: Can we just drop it darling?

Bill: No we can't. I hate you.

Jane: Bill, just please calm down. I will remember next time.

Bill: How can you when you have the mind of a goldfish? You won't remember.

Jane: Right, I have tried my best. You cook for yourself, set out the dining table for yourself and remember to place the fork on the RIGHT hand side yourself!

Bill: No, you do it. Remember to put my fork on the RIGHT, OK?

Jane: No Bill, go to your bedroom. I won't let you talk to me like this. I am your mother and you are forty-two years old so go get a girlfriend... Good luck in finding one who can stand your mouthing off.

Board 1 : 0 Me

Fridah Risper Nzaba

It was just before sunset that I went wishy-washy.

Right to left,

Up and down,

Woo hoooooo.

The reviving splashes full of salt hit my glowing skin. Shivered.

The priceless joy wrapped in my smile as I approached a colossal wave.

Splash.

I went down.

Board One : Me nil.

Never give up. Three words lingered as I went underneath my board.

Roaaarrr! I rose, only to get tackled down again the by the sea.

Not fair. I never win.

Young Black Enterprise

Fridah Risper Nzaba

I'm dark in complexion,
Not even close to perfection.
Walk with my head up in the clouds,
Wanting to stand out in the crowd,
Yet you look down on me,
Like an object you despise.
Even though I haven't done anything,
To make you spite me like you do.

Wear jeans and a hoodie,
And you assume I'm from the hood.
Walk in a shop,
You look at me in shock.
Aren't I supposed to be here?
I wonder when I hear the endless whispers;
Whispers of uncertainty,
Whispers of even my fellow peers.

Tears fall down on my face,
'Cause every day
I face the same distaste,
From people that I don't detest.
Anger would have taken over me
If I was lower than you,
But because I am better!
You best remember!
That you will be hurting people forever
If you continue acting like that,
Like I'm some sort of danger
Around your area. Simple.

I Remember

Isabel Perez

I remember when I was in town with you.

It was dark and peaceful and nothing could go wrong.

I remember the guitar man, Richard, outside Primark.

Fingerless gloves, an old hat and copper coins.

I remember when you offered him my Easter egg in exchange for guitar lessons.

He didn't take you seriously,

But we didn't care because it was a good night.

I remember the sound swirling around people and bringing them closer in.

I remember the two drunk men dancing, and the sound of you laughing.

I still remember your laugh.

We sang John Lennon's 'Imagine', and I looked up and sung it to the sky, to you and to Richard.

I remember walking through the empty streets, reaching into my pockets and finding my egg gone.

I remember not caring because it was a good night.

We walked further on, until it was time to go home.

I remember hugging you and not wanting to let go.

I remember that time, when you were my friend.

But do you remember me now?

Untitled!

Isabel Perez

Please do not see me as part of a competition.
I am a piece of creative writing, waiting for my creative reader.
I ask you not to compare me to others; I am not here to win.
Goodwill is something that competition cannot destroy.
So please take away all your selfishness, envies and insecurities and read this story again.
You will thank me one day and I will be waiting.
I am a story. I am your best friend.
I am waiting to complete you as an equal.
Keep on turning the page...

The Playground of Jealousy

Isabel Perez

All the boys hung out in one corner and the girls in the other. The boys would kick around an old football and parade their masculinity by seeing who could take the most Chinese burns to the same arm. The girls, however, twiddled their hair and secretly raised their skirts up every so often. Jenny even got hers above her knees.

'I dare you, go on!' came from one corner, and giggles from the other.

'Will you go out with me?' said Billy. He was a brave soldier, stepping out onto the battlefield.

I began to eat my sandwich.

'Oi! She's mine!'

Bobby came out of the shadows to claim his girl and received a swift kick to the leg from Billy.

One of the girls said how Bobby was braver than Billy.

Another girl said Billy was stronger.

Before I knew it, everyone was flirting.

I was in the playground of jealousy.

How Many Times Have You Played the Guitar?

Isabel Perez

How many times have you played the guitar to find it has no strings?
To stroke your hand across the hole and watch your palm sink in.
How many pictures have you seen, of people having fun?
To look in the mirror and see yourself and know you have no one.
You feel alone like no one cares and then you start to think
Of the friend you had; it makes you mad and your heart begins to sink.
How many times have you cried over something you couldn't mend?
How many stories could you tell of you and your friend?
Don't you fear, because love is near and you'll find it soon enough.
You are strong and beautiful and life is weak and rough.
You pick up your guitar, hold it close, and then begin to find
You're strumming strings, making music, and have left your friend behind.

Biographies: Sixth Form

Fridah Risper Nzaba

Fridah thinks Chinese babies are the cutest thing in the world. She likes London and Australian accents, although she can't do them, and secretly loves Habbo.com. Her favourite Smarties are the blue ones and if push came to shove she would marry Taylor Lautner's six-pack, even though her lucky number is seven. She wants to be an Electrical Engineer and is terrified of spiders, but has been known to talk to them.

Fatima S Khan

Fatima knows no fear and likes to listen to the rabab because she finds it soothing. Her favourite colours are blue, green and silver and she currently likes the letters 'S', 'H' and 'K' but her alphabetical preferences change constantly. In her spare time Fatima is a keen cook. She is quietly confident and was recently part of a group which entered a poster for a competition having secretly written the word 'Winner' on the back of it. Fortunately, it did!

Isabel Perez

When Isabel was ten, she had a pet caterpillar called Jim. Her secret pleasure is singing along to Mambo Number Five: 'I need a little Monica in my life...' Little Monicas, beware! In the cornflakes v Cheerio battle she's a cornflake girl every time. Her favourite animal is the squirrel because she'd like to climb trees. Samuel L Jackson is her hero, just for being cool, and her dream is to sit on a roof at midnight and play the guitar. She wants to be a photographer and her favourite letter of the alphabet is 'J'.

My Name Is...

Monet Dinall-Coley

My name is Monet Amender Medina Dinall-Coley. I hate my first name because I am not a man with a massive white beard. I am named after my auntie and my nana, and some people call me MoneT because of the way it is spelt.

BUT I am also proud of my name because my mum said she named me Monet because of the beautiful paintings by Claude Monet.

The Weather

Monet Dinall-Coley

As the sun shines, the heat targets your face and melts your feet to the ground.

All of a sudden, snow emerges from the sky and it's picked up by the wind, blowing everything in its path.

The cold comes in, the wind strikes your face sounding like a loud drum set.

Hail flies in the air smashing everything like furious stones.

The frost came in but was lost.

How to Live a Happy Life

Monet Dinall-Coley

To live a happy life you need to jump up and down six times, listen to music always, have fun, play the saxophone like a jazz star.

Fight with your brother, eat Chinese food and drink pop even though you're not allowed to, and complain about everything.

Oh, and don't forget to wash at the end of the day.

The Hurricane

Zachary C Douglas

On 16th August a mini tornado, or hurricane, hit my grandfather's farm. Unluckily, I was there. The thunder clap of this event echoed in time and space. I was chucked into the mighty storm of life and death. It was sucking the life-force out of me but I was yet again chucked out of it. The mighty tornado died in peace and no one else knew about it because it was on the tip of a tiny village near Thailand. I returned to England with my pride and honour, knowing I am stronger than a tornado.

Tsunami

Zachary C Douglas

In the awesome Hawaii in America: a tsunami as big as Mount Everest times ten billion. Flood. I grabbed my surf board and scuttled like a crab. I ran desperately then realised – why run when you can surf?

I waited for the water to hit the ground.

As it was right in front of me I jumped, with the cold sensation of the sea on my feet, and surfed my way across the States. I got to the airport in the nick of time because my plane back to England was about to leave. It was a race against time... Good news! I got on the plane heading for England and as it was around Christmas time I was eating mince pies throughout the trip back to Nottingham.

That was the end... or was it?

I didn't know, but the tornado from Thailand last year, which was sucking the life out of me, found me and followed me back to Nottingham and destroyed all the schools.

(No one was in them at the time).

Nick Parker Does Something Unexpected

Jake Lawrence Dunn

Nick Parker slipped on his jet-black clothing and his mask, only revealing his green and blue eyes, twinkling in the night sky.

He looked over the building one last time and plunged down towards the streetlights and the people below…

He used his hook to launch up into the air when suddenly –

BEEP! BEEP!

His phone began ringing and he took it out. Worst person that was calling: Grandma.

'Hi Granny,' Nick said, trying to subdue the irritation that was boiling in his stomach.

'Sweetie, I've got a problem with the computer – I can't find the files.'

Nick rolled his eyes.

'Go to My Files and…'

'YOUR files? They're mine!'

'Granny, what I mean is…'

Granny cut him off.

'It always has to be about you. I'm telling your mother!'

Oh man… Nick sighed, heading back home. *Looks like I'm grounded from being a ninja for two weeks*, he thought. *Great!*

Seasons

Jake Lawrence Dunn

In Autumn, you can always find a leaf,
You can hear them crunching beneath your feet.

Freezing as leaves turn into snow,
You can hear the wind whistle as it blows.

Tremor as you see a cloud
Become thunder, huge and loud.

Look around and suddenly see the conkers,
One drops on your head; will you go bonkers?

Sweating and dripping from the blistering heat,
Feel it start to boil on the bottom of your feet.

Back to the snow, see the white blanket of frost,
Stumble through the chalk-white forest,
You are lost…

How to Jump to the Moon

Jake Lawrence Dunn

---

1. First, buy a jetpack
2. Buy an astronaut helmet from Amazon (they're cheap now)
3. Go to Alton Towers and ride 'The Space Ride'
4. Once you're on the ride, put helmet and jetpack on
5. After about ten seconds, the ride will be whizzing up into the clouds
6. Use the momentum and jump (by the way, make sure the jetpack has batteries in it)
7. Use ultra-boost button on the jetpack to blast off into space
8. Land on the moon
9. Do the moonwalk
10. Think of a way to get back down…

I am...

Jake Lawrence Dunn

I am not a quiet little mouse,
I don't get up early in the house,
I'm not good at Maths at all, really,
I'm never going paragliding again! I nearly died!
Nearly...

I am a huge mass of messy hair,
I love horrors but can't watch them all. NOT FAIR,
I'm like a lion when angry, leave me alone,
I'm a big fan of texting, I love my phone! ☺

To Live a Happy Life You Need To:

Robyn Gill

---

1. Listen to your favourite music (I would suggest Black Veil Brides).
2. Try your hardest to achieve good levels in school.
3. Play the guitar and complete a full song to perfection (it will make you feel proud!).
4. Hang around with your friends – surely they can make you smile!
5. Enjoy every day like it's your last.
6. Treat yourself and others, wear clothes that make you feel happy and describe you.
7. Drink Coca-Cola whilst watching zombie movies.
8. Finally, eat food, don't listen to anything nasty people say and follow your dreams.

I am...

Robyn Gill

I am not naturally ginger.
I am naturally brown-haired instead.
I am not a girly girl, so if you think so you are insane.
I am a rocker.
Make sure you don't get in my way because I love playing my guitar,
And I'm head-banging your way!
I am loud!
I AM ME!

How to Train a Unicorn

Lucy Megan Guiblin

Hate having a disobedient unicorn? Read on to find out how to train one:

1. Never let unicorns eat rainbows, it will make them hyper, guaranteed.
2. Buy your unicorn an eskimo (but don't let the eskimo out of the cage).
3. First off, make your unicorn fly over your house with you riding it.
4. Secondly, spike their daily rainbow drops with pixie dust.
5. Your unicorn is nearly ready; just let the eskimo out of the cage now.
6. Give your unicorn a kitten to play with and then your unicorn is ready.
7. Make sure that when your unicorn is playing with the kitten it doesn't think it's a chew-toy.

Your unicorn is ready. If this doesn't work then I recommend taking your unicorn to the vet (the one over the rainbow, that is) to get him checked out. If in a few days you retry these steps and your unicorn fails, then I'm sorry to say this but your unicorn must be broken.

How to Prepare for a Trip to Mars

Kia Johnson-Norton

- Don't forget to feed the cat! It's not like the neighbours are actually going to feed it, no matter how much you pay them.

- Don't forget to stop at McDonalds before you get on the spaceship – or you'll regret it after being told they don't serve Happy Meals or burgers in Martian restaurants.

- Don't forget the cow, as she can provide you with milkshakes, ice-cream and butter. But remember to take your own grass because they don't have any on Mars.

I Am Not Amazing at Lying

Kia Johnson-Norton

I am not amazing at lying,
I am a leopard amongst a pack of cheetahs.
I am not afraid of flying.
I am always attempting to pick up the pieces.
I am tall enough to reach the shelf.
I am loud but quiet.
I could cause a riot.
All I am is myself.

When Julie Meets Rainbow

Nyall Wright

After a night of pounding my guitar the show was finally over. As I was about to exit the stage door I saw a shadow move into a shadow, so I decided to investigate.

'Hello, who's there? *there?*' My voice echoed in the shadow, and then I heard a faint 'Hello.'

As the shadow emerged from hiding I saw it was a fourteen year old boy.

'Hello, what's your name? It's OK, I won't bite.'

His reply was faint but I heard: 'M-m-m-m-my name is Rainbow Jones.'

How to Get Your Pet Talking Monkey, Steve, to Do What you Say

Nyall Wright

---

1. Give him treats.
2. Always involve him in your schemes.
3. Tell him all your secrets.
4. Teach him basic English.
5. Give him his own house.
6. Make him your best friend.
7. Never hit him if he does anything bad.
8. Don't feed him gummy bears.
9. Feed him unicorn drops.
10. Give him an Eskimo friend.
11. Don't let him drink.

Biographies: Year Seven Group

What's the beautiful sound I hear in the distance? Oh, that's **Monet Dinall-Coley** blasting some tunes out on her sax along to the film *Happy Feet*. Mon-Mon is a little accident-prone and has knocked herself out for over three minutes. She also had a rather nasty accident running at the swimming pool (that's what happens when you ignore the signs). Mysterious Monet has secrets but she isn't full of them. One thing that she's not secretive about is her dream of smashing a window. Watch out!

Zachary C Douglas, or Zack for short, is hiding a secret and it begins with the letter C. Though he won't reveal what his middle name is, he will admit his passion for pizza and piano-playing, and his love of the colour brown. You won't catch wild man Zack crying in public and he's happy to tussle with a tornado. As a child he used to play with snakes so as you can imagine he doesn't scare easily...

Jake Lawrence DUN DUN DUNN loves fancy dress. He loves it so much that he once turned up to school dressed as The Joker only to realise that it wasn't even dress up day – bless. He's a humble chap with simple tastes who enjoys singing, falling over and chasing after his cat whilst plotting how to achieve his ambition of one day being able to fly. If you can't find him he's probably hiding in a supermarket waiting till the coast is clear so he can run and jump into a supermarket trolley.

Robyn Gill is a normal girl with a normal nickname: Bob. Bob or Robyn is never happier than when eating a nice chicken korma; that is unless she's sucking a clothes label whilst listening to the Black Veil Brides. Robyn loves singing, drawing, gymnastics and playing the guitar and her favourite colour is black. This wannabe rock star is a tough cookie - so tough that she cried when she left Year Six.

Kia Johnson 'Twilight' Norton loves everything about Stephanie Meyer's books and the films them followed them, particularly Jacob. She loves listening to Cover Drive and watching My Big Fat Gypsy Wedding but she's terrified of caves. Poor Kia was once assaulted by a particularly violent ladder which explains her fear of them to this day.

Lucy Megan Guiblin is a funny blonde who's a big fan of munching on Coco-Pops and who, like Jake, has a history of dressing up when it's not strictly appropriate (you should see her Superman outfit). This Lana Del Ray-loving ice-skating superstar has always dreamed of being a forensic scientist; that is when she isn't jumping into poles or accidently soaking herself in the showers after P.E. Oooops.

Nyall Wright is a seriously rad skateboarding sort of dude. So rad in fact that if he ever saw a spider he would run away from it and hide immediately. Gnarly. Nyall's rarely happier than when sat in front of a *Family Guy* marathon with a pizza all to himself or when blasting out a bit of Slipknot on his guitar. He's essentially Nottingham's answer to Bam Margera and to begin his training for this role once threw himself down stairs.